Hercules
and Other
Greek Legends

Contents

HERCULES
AND THE HYDRA

WRITTEN BY BOB ESCHENBACH
AND TOM PIPHER
ILLUSTRATED BY RICHARD HOIT

Hercules lived in Greece a long, long time ago.
Hercules learned many things when he was a boy.
He learned how to shoot with a bow and arrow.
He learned how to fight with a sword.
He learned how to wrestle.
He was the strongest boy in Greece.
But most of all, Hercules learned how to think.

When Hercules grew up, he had many
very, very hard tasks that he had to do.
One of his tasks was to kill the Hydra.
The Hydra was a snake monster
with nine heads.
If any head was cut off,
the monster would grow
two more heads in its place.
The Hydra could not be killed
if it still had a head.

Hercules is a Roman name.
The Greek name for Hercules
was Heracles.

One day Hercules set out to slay the Hydra.
The Hydra lived in a swamp
with a big, big crab.
Hercules took his cape made of lion's skin,
his bow and arrow, and his sword.
He went all the way to the swamp.
There was the Hydra in the trees.
The nine heads were hissing.
Hercules held his bow and arrow.
He shot fire arrows into the trees
to get the Hydra out into the open.
He took his sword and cut off the first head,
but two more heads grew back.
He cut off some more heads, but each time
two more heads grew back again.
At the same time, the big, big crab
took a hold of Hercules's foot.

Then the Hydra bit Hercules,
but the bite would not go through the lion cape.
Hercules gave the big, big crab a kick
and reached for his fire torch.
Hercules was tired, so it was time to think.
He made a plan. He cut off a head
and put the fire torch on the headless neck.
This stopped the Hydra's head
from growing back.
Hercules cut off the other heads.
He put the fire torch on each headless neck.

Can you think of a
time when you were
tired so you had to
think of an easier
way to do something?

Soon there was only one head left.
Hercules and the Hydra got into a fight.
The Hydra got around Hercules's legs,
and they wrestled.
Hercules took the head off the Hydra
and put it under a rock.

The strongest man in Greece
had killed the Hydra!

Think back. How did Hercules become the strongest man in Greece?

12 Tasks
of Hercules

Written by Elizabeth Hookings
Illustrated by Richard Hoit

Killing the Hydra
was the second of twelve very hard tasks
that Hercules had to do.

> 1. Hercules had to kill a fierce lion.
> This lion had a skin so thick
> that no weapon could get through it.
> Hercules killed the lion with his hands.
> Then he put on the lion's skin
> to keep himself safe.

2. Killing the Hydra was Hercules's second task.
(You can read about Hercules and the Hydra
on pages 2–9.)

3. Hercules had to catch a deer with a net.
It took Hercules a year to catch the deer.

4. Hercules had to trap a big boar.
A boar is a wild hog that has tusks.
Hercules chased the boar into a deep snowdrift.
When the boar couldn't move, Hercules tied it with a rope.

11

Have you heard people talk about a Herculean task? What do you think it means?

5. Hercules had to clean the king's stables.
The stables had not been cleaned
for years and years.
Hercules made a dam on a river.
The water from the dam went into the stables
and cleaned them.

6. Hercules had to kill some man-eating birds.
He made a loud noise,
so the birds flew up in the air.
Then he shot the birds with his poison arrows.

What sport
these days uses
a bow and
arrows?

7. Hercules had to capture a bull on the island of Crete.

8. Hercules had to capture four horses that ate people.

9. Hercules had to get the belt of the Queen of the Amazons.
The person who had the belt on became very strong.
The Queen of the Amazons
said she would give the belt to Hercules.
But he had to fight the Amazon army to get the belt away.

10. Hercules had to get some cattle.
A two-headed dog and a giant looked after the cattle.
Hercules killed the dog and the giant,
and took the cattle.

11. Hercules had to get
some golden apples.
No one knew where to find the apples.
Atlas said he would get the apples
if Hercules would hold up the sky for him.
When Atlas came back with the apples,
he did not want to take the sky back.
Hercules tricked Atlas, took the apples,
and ran away.

If you were given
twelve very hard tasks
to do, what do you
think they might be?

12. Hercules had to bring back
a big dog with three heads.
Hercules put ropes on the three heads
and dragged the dog all the way home.

THE WOODEN HORSE OF TROY

WRITTEN BY ELIZABETH HOOKINGS
ILLUSTRATED BY RICHARD HOIT

Long, long ago,
the Greeks and the Trojans were fighting a war.

The Greeks said:
The war started because Paris, a Trojan prince,
kidnapped a Greek princess named Helen.
We sent a thousand ships to Troy.

The Trojans said:
The war started
because the Greeks
kidnapped a Trojan princess.
We took Helen to get even.
But Helen fell in love with Paris
and wanted to go to Troy.

After ten years of fighting, the Greeks said:
We were brave, and the Trojans were not.
The Trojans went back inside the gates of the city
because it looked as if they were going to lose the war.
We had a clever plan.
We built a big wooden horse.
Lots of our soldiers hid inside the horse.
We left the wooden horse where our camp had been.
Then the rest of us sailed away in our ships.
We hid behind an island.
The Trojans thought that we had given up and gone home.

How long do you think it took the Greeks to build the wooden horse?

After ten years of fighting, the Trojans said:
The Greeks knew that we were going to win,
so they gave up and went home.
They left behind a wooden horse.
We took the horse inside the gates of the city.
We thought we had won the war.

That night, the Greeks said:
Our ships sailed back when it was dark.
The soldiers who were in the wooden horse
came out when the Trojans were asleep.
They opened the gates of Troy.
We ran into the city.
We got Helen and took her back with us.

Have you heard the saying
"All's fair in love and war"?
Was what the Greeks
did fair?

That night, the Trojans said:
The wooden horse was a mean trick.
Most of our soldiers were killed in their sleep.
The Greeks could not beat us
without playing a mean trick.

THE REAL TROY

Some people think that the story of the Trojan War
grew from a real war between the Greeks and the Trojans.
People have searched where they think
the city of Troy would have been.
They found the ruins of more than one city.
People cannot say which of the cities that they found
would have been the city in the Trojan War.

MODERN GREECE

● TROY

● ATHENS

Did you know that there are planets
called the Trojan planets?
They have the names of some of the heroes
from Greece and Troy.
There are about forty Trojan planets.
They revolve around the sun
just like the earth does.
The Trojan planets are in the same orbit
as the planet Jupiter.

MODERN TURKEY

Find Greece on a map of the
world. Now find where Troy
might have been.

Achilles

Written by Sandra Iversen
Illustrated by Richard Hoit

Achilles was a Greek hero.
He lived a long, long time ago.
Soon after Achilles was born,
his mother dipped him into the River Styx.
The Greeks believed that the waters of the River Styx
kept them safe.
When Achilles's mother dipped him into the river,
she held him by his heel.
This was the only part of his body
that the water did not touch.

Why do you think
Achilles's mother
dipped him into the
River Styx?

When Achilles grew up, Greece was at war with Troy.
Achilles's mother did not want her son
to fight in the war.
But Achilles wanted to fight for his country.
He thought that he would be safe
because he had been dipped in the River Styx.

You can read more about the war between the Greeks and the Trojans on pages 16-23.

Achilles fought for a long time,
but then he left the war.
Achilles's best friend
wanted to look like Achilles
so that the Trojans would think
that Achilles was still fighting.
But Achilles's friend was killed by a Trojan prince
named Hector.

The name "Achilles tendon" comes from the Greek legend about Achilles. You can find your Achilles tendon at the back of your ankle. It holds your calf muscles to your heel bone.

Achilles was mad when his friend was killed
so he went back into the Greek army.
He killed Hector to get even.
He dragged Hector's body behind his chariot,
around the city of Troy.
The Trojan prince, Paris, wanted to get even, too,
so he shot a poison arrow at Achilles.
The arrow went into Achilles's heel.
It was the heel that had not been dipped
in the River Styx.
Achilles died.

Have you ever heard
someone say that
something was a
person's Achilles' heel?
What does that mean?

Index